EULENBURG AUDIO+SCORE

Camille Saint-Saëns

Concerto No. 1 for Violoncello and Orchestra in A minor / a-Moll

Op. 33

Edited by / Herausgegeben von
Hans-Hubert Schönzeler

EULENBURG

EAS 168
ISBN 978-3-7957-6575-0
ISMN 979-0-2002-2558-7

© 2010 Ernst Eulenburg & Co GmbH, Mainz
for Europe excluding the British Isles
Ernst Eulenburg Ltd, London
for all other countries
Edition based on Eulenburg Study Score ETP 1285
CD ℗ & © 1996 Naxos Rights International Ltd

Ernst Eulenburg Ltd
48 Great Marlborough Street
London W1F 7BB

Contents / Inhalt

Preface

Composed: 1872 in Paris
First performance: 19 January 1873 at the Société des Concerts du
Conservatoire in Paris
Original publisher: Durand & Fils, Paris
Instrumentation: 2 Flutes, 2 Oboes, 2 Clarinets, 2 Bassoons – 2 Horns,
2 Trumpets – Timpani – Strings
Duration: ca. 18 minutes

'Oddly enough, you can talk with musicians for hours about the music of France, yet it would never occur to anyone to mention the name Saint-Saëns.'[1] Thus the French writer and music critic Romain Rolland expressed his bewilderment at Saint-Saëns' neglect in turn-of-the-century France, a sentiment that reflects the country's general ambivalence towards her most Romantic composer. During his lifetime, Saint-Saëns initially enjoyed great popularity but later suffered from his countrymen's contempt. If his music was resisted and finally ignored, this was due not least to the fact that he was never part of a particular movement or school but remained true to his own aesthetic ideals and compositional style. As a result, works that had once seemed new and even revolutionary were decades later decried as reactionary. Outside France, conversely, Saint-Saëns was able to establish a reputation for himself, his music increasingly appreciated, except for those two periods when war-time tensions caused his reputation to sink in 1870–71 and again from 1914 to 1918.

Writing in the *Revue blanche* on 15 November 1901, Debussy noted that his colleague 'knows the musical universe better than anybody'.[2] Few other composers, it may be added, have left such an extensive and comprehensive corpus of works. Not only did he write symphonic and dramatic music, vocal and chamber works, piano music, military band music and ballet music, but also the first original soundtrack for a film, *L'assassinat du Duc de Guise* (1908). His concertos date from every period of his long life, extending, as they do, from his Violin Concerto in C major Op. 58, which he wrote in 1858 and which was later officially designated his Second Violin Concerto, to his Second Cello Concerto in D minor Op. 119 of 1902.

---

[1] Quoted by Michael Stegemann, *Camille Saint-Saëns und das französische Solokonzert von 1850 bis 1920* (Mainz, 1984), 10; trans. Ann C. Sherwin as *Camille Saint-Saëns and the French Solo Concerto from 1850 to 1920* (Portland, Oregon, 1991), 18. Stegemann's study continues to offer the best overview of the composer's concertante output.
[2] Claude Debussy, *Monsieur Croche et autres écrits*, ed. François Lesure (Paris, 1987), p. 57; trans. Richard Langham Smith as *Debussy on Music: The Critical Writings of the Great French Composer* (Ithaca, New York, 1977), 54: 'M. Saint-Saëns est l'homme qui sait le mieux la musique du monde entier.'

The genre as a whole owed a great deal to Saint-Saëns, for it had lost much of its prestige in 19th-century France and become the poor cousin of music, having sunk to the level of a purely virtuosic display vehicle, its goal, for the most part, being to provide orchestral backing for the soloist's brilliant pyrotechnics. Everything that departed from the medium's three-movement norm and from the orchestra's subordinate function and that distracted the audience from the soloist's playing was found to be puzzling and even disturbing by audiences and critics alike. As a result, Saint-Saëns' concertos were bound to encounter resistance for not only did they flout all formal expectations but they created a new and more balanced relationship between the solo instrument and the orchestra, thereby challenging the soloist's previous predominance. And yet so egregious did their perceived shortcomings appear that performances of these concertos were greeted by vociferous protests and derided by many of the critics of the time.

In 1872, following the political débâcle of the Franco-Prussian War and personal disappointment at the failure of his opera *La princesse jaune*, Saint-Saëns turned his attention to the cello, completing his First Cello Sonata in C minor Op. 32 and his First Cello Concerto in A minor Op. 33. He may even have worked on both pieces simultaneously. (It is striking in this context that 30 years later he worked on his Second Cello Sonata in F major Op. 123 and his Second Cello Concerto in D minor Op. 119 at more or less the same time.) We do not know why Saint-Saëns suddenly developed his interest in the cello, but it is conceivable that he was encouraged to write both works by the concerto's dedicatee, Auguste Tolbecque, who also gave its first performance. In much the same way Pablo de Sarasate inspired him to write a number of his works for violin and orchestra.

Saint-Saëns' First Cello Concerto was given its first performance by the Société des Concerts du Conservatoire on 19 January 1873. According to Jean Bonnerot, the society's long-standing secretary and later the composer's biographer, this was an honour rarely granted to living composers, who were felt to be 'intruders'.[3] The response was positive, and the *Revue et Gazette musicale de Paris* reported in detail on the 'new and important work' under the heading 'Nouvelles diverses':

'If Monsieur Saint-Saëns decides to remain on this path, which is one he has already explored with his Violin Concerto, his Trio in F and other works of lesser import, he is certain to win back many of the votes that he lost with the all-too-flagrant waywardness of a number of his earlier works.'

The anonymous critic hailed the piece as

'beautiful and good, admirable in its sentiments, perfect in its cohesion and with a form which, as usual, is of the greatest interest. Strictly speaking, it is a *Concertstück*, for its three

---

[3] Jean Bonnerot, *C. Saint-Saëns: Sa vie et son œuvre*, 2nd edn (Paris, 1922), 69: 'A la Société des Concerts du Conservatoire, le violoncelliste Auguste Tolbecque obtenait du Director Deldevez la permission de jouer (19 janvier) le *Concerto en la mineur* pour violoncelle, honneur, en ce temps-là, rarement accordé aux auteurs vivants, que l'on regardait comme des intrus.'

relatively short movements follow each other without a break. The orchestra plays an important role here, giving the work its symphonic character, a character to which every self-respecting concerto since Beethoven has aspired. The opening *Allegro* is brilliant and well characterized; distinguishing features are by no means abundant and are invariably notable for their fine style and good taste. The *Minuet* that follows is charming; its principal motif, stated by the violins *con sordino*, would be march-like in character if it were not in triple time; the solo cello soon adds a countermelody, and the movement as a whole creates a most felicitous impression. The opening of the final *Allegro* may be somewhat bland, but the ending is warm and interesting.'[4]

The reviewer ends by praising the soloist's contribution to the performance's overall success.

Among the First Cello Concerto's novel features are undoubtedly its formal structure. The work is no longer cast in three separate movements: instead the individual sections pass into each other without a break, resulting in a single movement – in first-movement sonata form – in which a minuet-like intermezzo functions as a point of repose. But even the very beginning of the work left its audience surprised, for there is no extended orchestral introduction to prepare for the soloist's entry. Rather, a *forte* chord for the accompanying ensemble is all that is required to usher in the impassioned first subject, which is entrusted to the soloist. But the latter does not have an exclusive say, as would have been the case in one of the old virtuoso concertos. When the reviewer of the first performance singled out Beethoven as Saint-Saëns' model and spoke of the work's 'symphonic character', he was referring to the orchestra's obvious involvement in the musical argument. The orchestral writing is translucent and lean-textured, avoiding the danger of overwhelming the soloist, while themes and motifs move effortlessly through the orchestra, solo winds and string groups engaging in dialogue with each other or with the soloist, notably from bar 139 of the opening section onwards. It comes as no surprise to read Adam Carse's encomium of the composer in his *History of Orchestration*: 'His light touch and restraint served Saint-Saëns particularly well when orchestrally accompanying solo instruments or solo voices; almost the only quite satisfactorily scored violoncello concerto by a 19th-century composer is his well-known work in A minor.'[5] And Saint-Saëns' perception of the way in which the function of the soloist had been transformed when compared to that in the flood of virtuoso concertos of the earlier period is clear

---

4 'Nouvelles diverses', *Revue et Gazette musicale*, Vol. XL/4 (26 Jan. 1873), 30: 'Si M. Saint-Saëns veut bien rester dans cette voie, qui est celle où nous avons rencontré déjà son concerto de violon, son trio en *fa*, et quelques autres œuvres de moindre portée, il ralliera certainement bien des suffrages que la divergence par trop flagrante des tendances de bon nombre de ses précédentes ouvrages entre eux lui avait aliénés. […] une belle et bonne œuvre, d'un sentiment excellent, d'une cohésion parfaite, et où la forme, comme d'habitude, offre le plus grand intérêt. C'est, à proprement parler, un *Concertstück*, car les trois morceaux, relativement courts, s'enchaînent. L'orchestre y joue le rôle important qui donne à l'œuvre le caractère symphonique auquel tend, depuis Beethoven, tout concerto qui se respecte. Le premier allegro est brillant, d'une allure bien caractérisée; les traits proprement dits n'y abondent pas, et ils sont toujours marqués au coin de la bonne facture et du bon goût. Le menuet qui suit est charmant; le motif principal, dit par les violons en sourdine, aurait le caractère d'une marche, sauf le rhythme ternaire; le violoncelle solo vient bientôt y ajouter un contre-chant, et le tout est du plus heureux effet. Le début de l'allegro final est assez indifférent; mais la terminaison est chaleureuse et intéressante.'

5 Adam Carse, *The History of Orchestration* (London, 1925; New York, 1964), 300.

from his remark that 'the solo in a concerto is a role that must be conceived and performed like a character in a drama'.[6]

Saint-Saëns' varied and creative approach to the formal models of his age, his radical break with traditional listening habits and his reappraisal of the roles of the soloist and the accompanying orchestra by investing both with equal status are all notable aspects of his achievement, more especially in his First Cello Concerto Op. 33, a work that is now one of the pillars of the cello repertory. If the French Romantic's works were often misunderstood during his lifetime, there is no longer any doubt about his importance for the development of French music in the 19th century as a whole.

Wolfgang Birtel
Translation: Steward Spencer

[6] Quoted by Émile Baumann, *Les grandes formes de la musique: L'Œuvre de Camille Saint-Saëns*, 2nd edn (Paris, 1923), 223: 'Le solo d'un concerto est un *rôle* qui doit être conçu et rendu comme un personnage dramatique.'

Vorwort

komponiert: 1872 in Paris
Uraufführung: 19. Januar 1873 in der Pariser Société des Concerts du Conservatoire
Originalverlag: Durand & Fils, Paris
Orchesterbesetzung: 2 Flöten, 2 Oboen, 2 Klarinetten, 2 Fagotte – 2 Hörner, 2 Trompeten – Pauken – Streicher
Spieldauer: etwa 18 Minuten

„Es ist sonderbar: Man kann stundenlang mit Musikern über die Musik Frankreichs sprechen, doch nie fiele es einem ein, den Namen Saint-Saëns zu erwähnen", wunderte sich der französische Schriftsteller und Musikkritiker Romain Rolland einmal.[1] Seine Verwunderung spiegelt die ambivalente Haltung Frankreichs ihrem romantischen Komponisten gegenüber deutlich wider: Zu Lebzeiten erfreute er sich zunächst großer Beliebtheit, wurde dann aber verachtet, bekämpft, totgeschwiegen, auch weil er sich keiner Strömung und Schule anschloss, seinen ästhetischen Ansichten und seinem Kompositionsstil treu blieb. Und so kam es, dass seine Werke zunächst neu, ja revolutionär wirkten, Jahrzehnte später aber als reaktionär verschrien waren. Im Ausland konnte sich Camille Saint-Saëns dagegen etablieren, gewann der Musiker zusehends an Anerkennung – sieht man einmal von den deutsch-französischen „Verstimmungen" während der Kriegsjahre 1870/71 sowie 1914–18 ab.

„Saint-Saëns ist […] ein Mann, der die Musik in- und auswendig kennt wie kein anderer", lobte Claude Debussy in der *Revue blanche* vom 15. November 1901 seinen Komponistenkollegen[2], und nur wenige, darf man hinzufügen, haben ein derartig umfangreiches und alle Gattungen abdeckendes Gesamtwerk hinterlassen wie er: Symphonische und dramatische Musik, Vokal- und Kammermusik, Klavier-, Militär- und Ballettmusik hat Camille Saint-Saëns komponiert, aber auch mit *L'assassinat du Duc de Guise* 1908 die erste originale Filmmusik geliefert. Der Komposition von Solokonzerten widmete er sich zeit seines Lebens: vom Violinkonzert in C-Dur op. 58 (1858), das später die offizielle Nummer 2 erhielt, bis zu seinem zweiten Violoncellokonzert in d-Moll op. 119 (1902). Saint-Saëns verdankt die Gattung wesentliche Impulse, hatte sie doch im 19. Jahrhundert in Frankreich erheblich

---

[1] Zit. nach Stegemann, Michael: *Camille Saint-Saëns und das französische Solokonzert von 1850 bis 1920*, Mainz 1984, S. 10. Es bietet im Übrigen den besten Einblick in das konzertante Œuvre des Komponisten.

[2] „M. Saint-Saëns est l'homme qui sait le mieux la musique du monde entier." – Debussy, Claude: *Monsieur Croche. Sämtliche Schriften und Interviews*, hrsg. v. François Lesure. Aus dem Französischen übertr. v. Josef Häusler, Stuttgart 1974, S. 54.

X

an Ansehen verloren und war zum Stiefkind kompositorischer Beschäftigung geworden: Solokonzerte waren zum reinen Virtuosenstück herabgesunken, ihr kompositorisches Ziel war in erster Linie, dem brillierenden Solisten eine Orchester-Klangfolie zu bieten. Alles, was von der dreisätzigen Normalform und der untergeordneten Orchesterfunktion abwich, was die Aufmerksamkeit vom Solisten ablenkte, irritierte das Publikum (und die Musikkritik) oder störte gar. Da mussten die Solokonzerte von Saint-Saëns Anstoß erregen, denn einerseits durchbrachen sie den formalen Schematismus, andererseits brachten sie die absolute Vorherrschaft des Soloinstruments über den Orchesterpart in ein neues, nun ausgewogeneres Verhältnis – so sehr, dass es nicht nur zu Kritikerverrissen, sondern auch zu lautstarken Skandalaufführungen kam.

Im Jahre 1872, nach dem politischen Desaster des deutsch-französischen Krieges und nach einer persönlichen Niederlage des Komponisten, nämlich dem Misserfolg seiner ersten Oper *La princesse jaune*, beschäftigte sich Saint-Saëns mit solistischen Violoncellowerken: Er vollendete seine erste Sonate (c-Moll, op. 32) und sein erstes Konzert (a-Moll, op. 33). Möglicherweise arbeitete er an beiden Werken gleichzeitig. (Auffällig übrigens, dass auch die zweite Sonate, F-Dur, op. 123, und das zweite Konzert, d-Moll, op. 119, dreißig Jahre später in unmittelbarer zeitlicher Nachbarschaft geschrieben wurden.) Einzelheiten, warum sich der Komponist plötzlich mit dem Violoncello in Kammermusik und Solokonzert auseinandersetzte, sind nicht bekannt. Es ist aber durchaus denkbar, dass ihn der Widmungsträger und Uraufführungssolist des Konzertes, Auguste Tolbecque, dazu animierte, genauso, wie ihn Pablo de Sarasate zur Komposition von orchesterbegleiteten Violinwerken überredete.

Am 19. Januar 1873 wurde das erste Violoncellokonzert in der Société des Concerts du Conservatoire uraufgeführt: Dies war – nach Jean Bonnerot, dem langjährigen Privatsekretär und späteren Biografen von Saint-Saëns – eine Ehre, die damals nur selten noch lebenden Komponisten zuteil wurde, da sie als „Eindringlinge" gesehen wurden[3]. Die Resonanz war positiv und die *Revue et gazette musicale de Paris* berichtet in der Rubrik *Nouvelles diverses* ausführlich von dem „neuen und wichtigen Werk von M[onsieur] Camille Saint-Saëns":[4]

[3] „A la Société des Concerts du Conservatoire, le violoncelliste Auguste Tolbecque obtenait du Directeur Deldevez la permission de jouer (19 janvier) le *Concerto en la* mineur pour violoncelle, honneur, en ce temps-là, rarement accordé aux auteurs vivants, que l'on regardait comme des intrus […]" – Bonnerot, Jean: *C. Saint-Saëns: Sa vie et son œuvre*, 2. ergänzte Ausgabe, Paris 1922, S. 69.

[4] „Si M. Saint-Saëns veut bien rester dans cette voie, qui est celle où nous avons rencontré déjà son concerto de violon, son trio en *fa*, et quelques autres œuvres de moindre portée, il ralliera certainement bien des suffrages que la divergence par trop flagrante des tendances de bon nombre de ses précédentes ouvrages entre eux lui avait aliénés. […] une belle et bonne œuvre, d'une sentiment excellent, d'une cohésion parfaite, et où la forme, comme d'habitude, offre le plus grand intérêt. C'est, à proprement parler, un *Concertstück*, car les trois morceaux, relativement courts, s'enchaînent. L'orchestre y joue le rôle important qui donne à l'œuvre le caractère symphonique auquel tend, depuis Beethoven, tout concerto qui se respecte. Le premier allegro est brillant, d'une allure bien caractérisée; les traits proprement dits n'y abondent pas, et ils sont toujours marqués au coin de la bonne facture et du bon goût. Le menuet qui suit est charmant; le motif principal, dit par les violons en sourdine, aurait le caractère d'une marche, sauf le rhythme ternaire; le violoncelle solo vient bientôt y ajouter un contre-chant, et le tout est du plus heureux effet. Le début de l'allegro final est assez indifférent; mais la terminaison est chaleureuse et intéressante." – Ausgabe der *Revue et gazette musicale de Paris* XL/1873, No. 4, S. 30.

„Sollte M. Camille Saint-Saëns weiterhin diesen Weg beschreiten wollen, auf dem wir ihn schon mit seinem Violinkonzert, dem Trio in F und einigen anderen weniger bedeutenden Werken gesehen haben, so wird er sicherlich vieles von der Zustimmung bei den Menschen zurückgewinnen, die er mit einigen seiner letzten Werke durch allzu krasse Abweichung vom Modegeschmack verloren hatte."

Der Kritiker lobt dann das Konzert als

„ein hervorragendes Werk, von ausgezeichnetem Sentiment und vollkommener Geschlossenheit, in dem überdies die Form [...] von besonderem Interesse ist. Es handelt es sich hier genau genommen um ein *Concertstück*, da die drei relativ kurzen Teile ineinander übergehen. Das Orchester spielt dabei die wichtige Rolle, die dem Werk jenen sinfonischen Charakter verleiht, zu dem seit Beethoven jedes Konzert tendiert, das einen gewissen Anspruch erhebt."

„Das eröffnende Allegro ist brillant und von markantem Tempo; es gibt keinen Überfluss an musikalischen Einfällen, und sie sind stets geprägt durch guten Aufbau und Geschmack. Das folgende Menuett ist hübsch; das von gedämpften Violinen angestimmte Hauptthema könnte Marschcharakter haben, wenn es nicht im Dreiertakt stünde; das Solo-Violoncello stimmt schon bald eine Gegenmelodie an, und das Ganze ist von beglückender Wirkung. Der Beginn des Schluss-Allegros wirkt recht unentschlossen, aber das Ende ist warm und interessant."

Die Leistung des Solisten wird in den abschließenden Zeilen herausgehoben.

In der Tat: Neu war in diesem Konzert die formale Anlage, die Auflösung der üblichen Dreisätzigkeit. Saint-Saëns lässt die Teile ineinander übergehen, und eigentlich ist das Konzert ein einziger Satz (in Sonatenhauptform), in den der Komponist als Ruhepunkt das menuettartige Intermezzo eingebunden hat. Doch das Pariser Publikum war auch schon vom Beginn des Konzerts überrascht, denn keine ausgiebige Orchestereinleitung bereitete den Auftritt des Soloinstrumentes vor, nein, nach einem Forte-Schlag des Begleitensembles stieg der Solist gleich mit dem Hauptthema in passioniertem Tone ein. Aber er hatte nicht – in alter Virtuosenmanier – das alleinige „Sagen": Wenn der Kritiker der Uraufführung auf das Beethoven-Vorbild, auf den „sinfonischen Charakter" verweist, ist damit der starke Einbezug des Orchesters in das musikalische Geschehen gemeint. Im durchweg aufgelockerten und durchsichtigen Instrumentationsstil, der das Soloinstrument klanglich nicht zudeckt, lässt der Komponist dabei Themen und Motive durch das Orchester wandern, solistische Bläser oder Strichergruppen miteinander und mit dem Solo dialogisieren, deutlich etwa im ersten Teil ab Takt 139. Kein Wunder, wenn Adam Carse in seiner *The History of Orchestration* schreibt: „Seine leichte Hand und seine Zurückhaltung dienten Saint-Saëns besonders bei der Orchesterbegleitung von Soloinstrumenten oder Solostimmen" und dem Violoncello-Konzert in a-Moll attestiert, dass es „das einzige gelungen instrumentierte Violoncello-Konzert eines Komponisten aus dem 19. Jahrhundert"[5] sei. Und wie verändert der französische Musiker die

---

[5] Carse, Adam: *The History of Orchestration*, New York 1925, Reprint 1964, S. 300.

Funktion des Solisten – im Vergleich zur Flut von Virtuosenkonzerten – sah, zeigte sich in seinem Ausspruch: „Das Solo eines Konzertes ist wie eine Rolle, die als dramatische Person verstanden und gegeben werden muss."[6]

Der variative und kreative Umgang mit den Formmodellen seiner Zeit, mit dem Brechen von überkommenen Hörgewohnheiten und mit der Aufwertung von Solopart *und* Orchesterbegleitung durch ein gleichberechtigtes Miteinander – dies macht die Leistung des französischen Romantikers Camille Saint-Saëns aus, ganz besonders im ersten Violoncellokonzert op. 33, das zu einem Klassiker der Violoncelloliteratur geworden ist. Blieb das Œuvre des Komponisten zu Lebzeiten vielfach unverstanden, steht seine Bedeutung heute für die Entwicklung der französischen Musik im 19. Jahrhundert außer Frage.

Wolfgang Birtel

---

[6] „Le solo d'un concerto est un *rôle* qui doit être conçu et rendu comme un personnage dramatique." – Zit. nach Baumann, Émile: *Les grandes formes de la musique: L'Œuvre de Camille Saint-Saëns*, 2. ergänzte Ausgabe, Paris 1923, S. 223.

Cello Concerto No. 1

Camille Saint-Saëns
(1835–1921)
Op. 33

EAS 168

© 2010 Ernst Eulenburg Ltd, London
and Ernst Eulenburg & Co GmbH, Mainz

2

3

4

6

9

EAS 168

18

20

21

EAS 168

EAS 168

24

27

29

EAS 168

32

38

42

43

EAS 168

48

51

52

54

56

58

63

EAS 168

66

Printed in China